CW00850719

PERKIN WARBECK

Author biography

Robert Hume lives in Broadstairs and teaches history and psychology at Clarendon House Grammar School, Ramsgate, where he also runs the school Scrabble club and the football teams. His historical novel, *Ruling Ambition: The Story of Perkin Warbeck,* was published by Gee & Son in 2000.

WHO WAS...

Perkin
WARBECK

*The Boy who would
be King*

ROBERT HUME

Illustrations by Alex Fox

First published in 2005 by
Short Books
15 Highbury Terrace
London N5 1UP

10 9 8 7 6 5 4 3 2 1

Copyright ©
Robert Hume 2005

Robert Hume has asserted his right under the Copyright,
Designs and Patents Act 1988 to be identified as the
author of this work. All rights reserved. No part of this
publication may be reproduced, stored in a retrieval
system or transmitted in any form, or by any means
(electronic, mechanical, or otherwise) without
the prior written permission of both the copyright
owners and the publisher.

A CIP catalogue record for this book
is available from the British Library.

Illustration copyright © Alex Fox 2005
Quiz by Sebastian Blake

ISBN 1-904977-13-8

Printed in Great Britain by
Bookmarque Ltd., Croydon, Surrey

FOREWORD
Prince or pretender?

In 1483, King Edward IV of England died leaving two sons, Prince Edward, aged 12, and Prince Richard, aged 10. The throne was then seized by the boys' uncle who became king, as Richard III. Soon war broke out when Henry Tudor claimed the throne. And at the Battle of Bosworth in 1485 Richard III was killed and Henry Tudor was crowned King Henry VII of England.

About this time, rumours began to spread that the princes had been murdered on the orders of their late uncle, Richard III. However, some people believed that the man who had been given the job of killing Prince Richard had not had the courage to do it and had helped him to escape.

In the days before cameras and television, dental

records and DNA testing, who would be able to tell the real prince from an impostor? Suppose a boy of similar age and appearance to Richard was to pretend that he was the missing prince?

This is the daring adventure story of a boy from Flanders, who tries to trick the rulers of Europe into believing that he is Prince Richard – that he miraculously escaped from the Tower of London and has been living in hiding, waiting for the right moment to claim the throne of England.

CHAPTER 1

Late November, 1499: Perkin's forehead throbbed, his bones ached. When he tried to move, the chains that bound him bit into his ankles. He felt very, very cold.

A rough voice echoed along the passageway: 'Rogues. Wake up!' Perkin could almost smell the gaoler's foul and pungent breath.

'Leave a man to his sleep!' someone grunted.

Was it really morning? Who knew? Only a trace of light filtered into his stinking cell, deep within the green slimy walls of the Tower of London.

Perkin, a young man, just twenty-five years old, had been accused of impersonating Prince Richard, the younger of the two missing princes. He had been brought to the Tower as a criminal who had plotted the downfall of King Henry VII and had attempted to seize the throne for himself. He was now awaiting trial, charged with high treason.

So many prisoners before him had faced tortures of such unimaginable horror that they had confessed to whatever their captors wanted. A deep sense of dread shot through Perkin as he thought of how some of these confessions had been obtained – by squeezing hands in presses until bones broke, by ripping flesh open with sharp needles. Still worse lay in store for some poor souls who were dragged from their cells in the dead of night, taken to the White Tower and there stretched on the rack until their limbs were pulled out of their sockets. Could that be the terrible fate that awaited him? Perkin's future hung in the balance. He hoped desperately for a reprieve. The next few days would determine whether he would be given one.

Propping himself up on his elbow, he tried to think back to the happier times of his childhood. He had grown up in the bustling town of Tournai in Flanders. If he concentrated hard enough, he could hear the cries of the tradesmen selling cloth and carpet in the marketplace, and the dogs barking around the stalls. He could picture the group of actors who performed plays from a cart in the street and the lush green fields that surrounded the town. He remembered how his cousin had taught him to read the Bible, to write his name and add up numbers.

Perkin's thoughts turned to his mother, whom he had not seen since he was ten years old. He remembered her now, sitting beside her as she sewed, feeling the silky texture of the fabrics as they brushed against his skin. He would tell her how he looked forward to travelling to distant lands and having adventures at sea. However, all that his mother wanted was for him to become a cloth merchant, marry a local girl, settle down and raise a family. All very boring, Perkin had thought.

It was on a winter's morning when he was about nine years old, that his mother's plans for him had started to go very wrong. Perkin was watching his grandfather chop wood for the kitchen fire. It was only an hour or two before midday, and a cauldron of stew stood uncooked on the floor.

'Peterkin!' His grandfather called out his pet name. 'I've cut my hand. Run to fetch me a cloth, there's a good little fellow.'

Perkin raced off to find a large handkerchief from his mother's linen box at the top of the house. When he returned he bound it across his grandfather's palm. But it was not long before a small bright red stain began to appear through the bandage. His grandfather stared at it.

'Noble blood!' he declared solemnly.

'What do you mean?' asked Perkin.

'Noble blood! We are descended from the Farous. We were an important family at one time, you know.'

'Merchants? Like those men who live in the tall, overhanging houses?'

His grandfather chuckled. 'No, much more important than that, Peterkin. So important that the kings of France would ask the Farous for advice.'

Perkin gasped.

'Of course, we are just has-beens these days. I am only a gatekeeper as you know.'

'But grandfather! Could...'

His grandfather put a finger to his lips to silence Perkin. He looked him straight in the eye.

'If the Farous are ever to become great again, it's up to you, my lad!'

CHAPTER 2

Perkin rested his back against the mildewed wall of his cell and closed his eyes. He remembered his first visit to London with his father who was supplying carpets to the royal court. It must have been springtime, as the floors of the house they stayed in were sprinkled with white blossom. He remembered London Bridge with its little houses and shops; the Palace of Westminster; and the sombre outlines of the Tower that was now his prison.

Then, when he was ten years old, Perkin had been taken to the bustling city of Antwerp, by Master Berlo, a merchant friend of his parents. Berlo had been looking for a handsome young man to help display the fine clothes he sold by actually wearing them. In Antwerp, parading Master Berlo's wares, Perkin heard customers talking of exotic lands full of spices, and islands where streams ran with gold. He would happily have listened to these tales day after day, had he not suddenly been struck down with a fever. For several months he was unable to work, and Berlo was forced to replace him.

When Perkin recovered, he went to look for work in the nearby town of Middelburg, and found a position as an apprentice to a cloth-seller. But he thought the town dull compared to Antwerp, and his new master mean.

One night he decided to run away from his house. And so it was that in 1488, at the age of fourteen, with no home and no job, Perkin began the life of a wanderer.

* * *

On a blazing hot summer afternoon later that year, some twenty miles away in the market place in Malines, Perkin was standing by a stall, deep in conversation with other customers about the rolls of silk and velvet on display.

Suddenly he heard a soft, well-spoken voice behind him, asking how much the silk was. When he turned, he found himself face to face with a finely dressed man. The nobleman had mistaken him for the stall-owner, and Perkin quickly put him right.

'Stall-holder or not,' the nobleman smiled, 'you seem to know something about fabrics.'

Perkin gave a little bow.

The nobleman raised an eyebrow. 'I work for the Duchess Margaret of Burgundy,' he said. 'She relies on me to supply items for her wardrobe. I think she might be interested to meet someone with your experience. And you would benefit greatly from the introduction. If you wish, I can arrange an audience for you with the Duchess.'

At first Perkin was too stunned to speak. Eventually he managed a hoarse whisper: 'I would be honoured, sir.'

'One more thing. Remember to take great care over your appearance and manners. First impressions always count with the Duchess.' The nobleman turned and left.

Two days later, and having taken the utmost care over his appearance and manners, Perkin was in Malines at the Duchess's court – a court that was the envy of Europe. From here she ruled over many wealthy lands and the place buzzed with officials, ambassadors and secretaries.

'Perkin Warbeck!' called out a courtier.

Perkin stepped forward and was led down a long corridor until they reached a heavy door. When he was told to enter, he did so hesitantly. The wall tapestries gleamed in the sunlight but there was nobody in the room.

Suddenly a small door opened at the far end and a lady entered, severe in manner and grandly dressed. She trod carefully, as if stepping on glass. Perkin felt himself being pushed forward by the courtier. He must bow.

As he straightened himself, he saw another lady

behind the first. It was then that he realized his mistake, for this second lady was obviously the Duchess Margaret. She was tall and slim, very straight backed and dressed elegantly in black velvet trimmed with gold lace. The Duchess dismissed her lady-in-waiting with a wave of her hand. She stared directly at Perkin; her tone was solemn. 'You are Perkin Warbeck?'

'Yes, Your Grace.'

'I am looking for a young man with experience of fabrics and eager to learn more.'

Her face was long and serious, her dark grey eyes seemed fierce. Perkin found it difficult to look directly at her, and focused instead on a gold chain around her neck.

'I need someone who can advise my tailors and seamstresses, someone able to represent my court abroad. I hear you have travelled. Which places do you know?'

Perkin's eyes moved from her gold chain to a great marble fireplace. He saw a crest featuring a chained falcon – the emblem of the Duchess's family, the House of York.

'I know Tournai where I was born, and Antwerp, Middelburg and London, Your Grace.'

'London?'

'Yes, I went with my father who was there to lay carpets at court.'

The Duchess's eyes widened. 'Whose court do you mean? That of my dear brother Edward – God bless his memory – or that of Henry Tudor, that man who calls himself king?'

'That of King Edward, Your Grace.'

'Really!'

The Duchess's tone became bitter: 'Henry has deprived me of the money and land my dear Edward promised me.'

She looked directly at Perkin: 'But you perhaps can help return my family to power in England.'

Perkin was bewildered. How on earth could he, a mere nobody, be part of any plan?

'Yes, you will do very well… I can see the likeness.'

What likeness, thought Perkin? Was this woman stark raving mad?

'You resemble him. You are tall and have his long blonde hair. Your manners are fair and you have the airs of a man of noble birth.'

Perkin was too amazed to say anything. What could she possibly have in mind?'

There was a long pause. The Duchess looked at Perkin strangely. Eventually she began to make everything horribly clear. 'My dear nephew Richard has not been seen for several years now. In fact, many believe he is dead. But this is not so. He is still very much alive, as you are going to prove!

'Here, at my court, you will be taught to speak English and be told everything you need to know about your family and the names of your household when you were a little boy. I shall expect you to learn every little detail by heart. Then, when I am ready, I shall send you away, to Ireland, a country that will welcome you, as it hates Henry Tudor, a country far enough away for you to work in safety. After you have had time to test out your abilities, to convince the Irish that you are Prince Richard, I shall send for you. I shall welcome you as my long lost nephew.'

Perkin was speechless; he felt bewitched by her. She had chosen him to defend the rights of her family and promised him great rewards. Her plans offered him riches and adventure beyond his wildest dreams. He recalled his grandfather's prophecy about his family's noble blood, that it was up to him to restore its fortunes. This was a sign that he could not ignore. Fate was pointing him in the direction of glory. But how could such a scheme possibly succeed?

The Duchess interrupted his thoughts. 'Naturally,

when you become King of England, I shall expect you to pay me all the money and land my brother promised me.'

The Duchess's lips tightened and a steely note entered her voice: 'Well boy? You have said nothing!'

Overwhelmed, Perkin fell on one knee before her.

'Your Grace, you do me a great honour. I promise to serve you in whatever way I can.'

'Will you swear to this over the bones of a saint?'

Perkin bowed his head in agreement.

The bargain was sealed. There was now no going back.

CHAPTER 3

A message soon came from Duchess Margaret: 'Go to Ireland. You will get help there from two important earls.' And so, on a mild autumn day Perkin boarded ship for Cork.

Before they set sail, an old and very wrinkled priest muttered some prayers for a safe journey. They had not been sailing long, however, before the sky became overcast and the sea turned rough. The wind split their tiny sail into shreds. All they could do was pray. Three days and nights passed as the ship rocked and swayed in the angry sea. What a relief when finally the rocky coast of Ireland emerged out of the early morning mist.

The next day the two earls and their men arrived.

'My lord of Warwick,' said one earl with a bow. 'Welcome to these safe shores!'

The earl had been misinformed by some people in Cork that Perkin was the Earl of Warwick, the same man they had seen in Cork some years earlier.

'I'm not the Earl of Warwick!' Perkin blurted out.

There was an embarrassed pause.

'Well, you must be King Richard's bastard son then' said the other earl.

Perkin grew impatient: 'Surely you recognize me?'

Eventually one man fell to his knees. 'Your appearance and royal bearing fit the description of the late King Edward. You must be his heir, sir, Prince Edward.'

'No, I am his brother, Richard. Prince Edward was killed on the orders of our wicked Uncle Richard. But the man who was looking after me showed mercy and helped me to escape. Sirs, I am depending on your support to help me regain my rightful throne.'

'I beg your pardon, Prince Richard, for not recognizing you at once.'

Nods and smiles followed, all from men whom Perkin had never seen before in his life.

Perkin was given lodgings with a merchant who had a house by the river. During the following weeks he met the earls several times; but they were not keen to discuss the Duchess's plan to make him King of England, saying it was too risky because King

Henry's spies were everywhere.

Many months passed until one night, when Perkin was getting ready for bed, there was a terrific banging on the street door. Candle in hand, he went down to see what the commotion was about.

Two men in dark cloaks stood on the step. One of them gave a little bow and handed over a small roll of paper. As he broke open the seal, Perkin's heart started to race. He was speechless. The King of France was asking him to come to Paris. Was this, perhaps, the Duchess Margaret's doing? Either way, he must obey the call.

* * *

Perkin sailed to St Malo. From here he was taken to the great city of Paris – all gables, church spires and grand buildings with towers. The coachman touched the reins lightly, and the carriage came to a halt on the stony driveway outside a palace. A servant came forward.

'Welcome, Duke of York! The King wishes to see you right away. Please come this way.'

Perkin was led through the Guards' Room with its dazzling assortment of swords, lances and axes, into various waiting rooms and past servants who bowed. Eventually they reached the waiting room to the King's special chamber. The servant crossed to a door on the other side of the room where he tapped out a special knock.

Perkin did not know what to expect. He was still unsure why the King of the most important country in Europe had asked to see him.

The servant returned. 'The King is ready for you!' Then, lowering his voice, he whispered 'Be prepared for his appearance.'

Perkin gasped. King Charles was a frail, sickly creature, with a big head and a small flabby neck – a bit like a ball balanced dangerously on top of a pillar.

Perkin knelt before him. 'Thank you, Your Majesty, for inviting me to your court.'

Charles clenched and unclenched his fists. Perkin looked up. The King's lips were thick and coarse. His eyes bulged. 'I think I c-c-c-can help you… s-s-s-sir, and there are m-m-m-many others at court who can ass-ss-ssist you too.'

Perkin felt very ill at ease. What should he say?

A bell sounded in the distance. It was time they took their places at table, tuck into succulent meats and game, moist cheeses, apples and pears. Discussions would have to be postponed until later.

* * *

The days passed and Perkin continued to be pampered at court, but he heard nothing about invading England. In fact, the talk was about attacking Naples in Italy. Eventually, one evening, the King summoned Perkin to his private suite. The King said nothing. It seemed that Perkin was expected to start.

'Your Majesty, I have been trained to impersonate Prince Richard, the younger son of the late King Edward. To this end I have been taught English, and can read a document and dictate a letter. The Duchess Margaret has told me how to address important ambassadors from overseas. I know how to give orders to servants: from the water-bearer who prepares the royal bath-tub, all the way down to the humblest page and kitchen scullion. I know how to enter a room without tripping over my shoes, when to bow and how not to spill my wine or slurp my soup.'

The King's face was blank.

Perkin decided he had to go on. 'I can ride a horse and wield a sword as well as any other prince can. I am ready to lead an army against England. Majesty, I seek your blessing, your support...'

The King's face stayed blank. Surely he was interested in a scheme against his old enemy, England.

The King cleared his throat. 'Henry is a m-m-m-most wicked man... he has ss-ss-ss-eized the th-th-throne from the true king!'

'Your Majesty! There can be no doubt...'

'I ass-ss-ure you I... will do everything in my power t-t-t-to ass-ss-st you and restore fair laws.'

How relieved Perkin was to hear these words. To have the backing of the most important prince in Europe gave him courage and strength.

Yet within a week he had been dismissed from court! At first he was completely baffled. Later he discovered that France had made peace with England! This meant that he could be in danger. What if King Charles had to send him to England as a prisoner as part of the agreement? He must flee from Paris immediately.

He seized one of the King's horses and galloped out of the city. Bonfires blazed in the streets to mark the peace with England. But Perkin had no reason to celebrate. He felt utterly neglected, his hopes dashed to pieces. And he had let the French King in on the secret. What now?

* * *

Perkin set off for Malines where he knew the Duchess of Burgundy would help him. Winter was beginning to set in, and dark grey clouds threatened to bring snow. He was anxious to complete the journey as soon as possible.

He arrived in Malines feeling exhausted, and with no money. The Duchess greeted him in her private chamber.

'Richard! I thought I would never see you again.'

That was Perkin's cue. 'My dear aunt!' he began. But his words sounded false.

'How good it is to see you again, dear nephew! You must be tired. You have had a long journey, and it is best that you now rest. I have a house where you can stay and I have drafted in a special guard, thirty men in all. You will recognize them immediately as they are dressed in blue and purple.'

* * *

Little by little, Perkin became used to the frantic pace of life at Malines. A great many people lived at court: servants, ladies-in-waiting, seamstresses, the Duchess even had her own priests. Secretaries came and went with orders for her to check and despatch to the far corners of her lands. The Duchess always scrutinized such correspondence very carefully: she had a frightful temper and usually insisted that changes be made.

Besides those who lived at court, there were many who visited daily – ambassadors from overseas, astrologers who would advise the Duchess when it was best to go into battle, and physicians who would worry over her health and once a month would bleed her – whether she needed it or not.

Every so often there was a banquet, and sometimes the guests wore masks. Sweet-scented rushes would be strewn across the floor at the far end of the grand hall, so that the less important guests could sit down without dirtying their clothes. But Perkin was always treated as a guest of honour, and was served at high table in the company of princes and important ambassadors.

One evening a relative of the Duchess's, Archduke Maximilian of Austria, was placed next to Perkin at dinner. A particularly large number of courses were offered that night in his honour. There was pork and lamb (roasted whole on a spit), peacock, swans, geese and pheasant – all cooked to perfection in rich fruity sauces. Accompanying the meal were great goblets of wine from the casks lining the palace cellars. As they ate, the Duchess's minstrels sung from a gallery above them and an acrobat performed cartwheels across the hall.

During the meal the conversation turned to the war between France and Italy and the troubles between the Scots and the English. Maximilian made it clear that he hated King Henry because he had seized the throne of England illegally. He listened with great interest as Perkin talked about the Duchess's plans for him.

Although the hour was late when they finished eating, it was still light outside so Perkin and Maximilian took a walk in the rose gardens. Perkin told him how he hoped to get the blessing of other countries. By the time they returned to the palace there was no doubt in Perkin's mind that Maximilian would help him. Maximilian was an ambitious man who wanted to extend his power and influence in Europe. Therefore, in return for his support, Perkin was made to promise that, should he die without a male heir, Maximilian would receive all Perkin's lands.

Before the month was out there was better news still, as the rulers of the Netherlands, Denmark and Scotland had all recognized Perkin as the rightful King of England. Perkin doubted that these men believed his claims to be Prince Richard – like Maximilian they would be expecting something in return – but what did it matter when he had their support?

By the end of 1494 the Duchess had spent about eighty thousand crowns on Perkin's behalf. Some of this money had been used to pay her agents to get support for Perkin in Ireland and Scotland. Most of it had been raised ready to equip a great expedition to England. Now she thought it was high time to make sure that she got something back for her money. So she got a legal contract drawn up. This said that when Perkin was crowned King of England he would, among other things, repay her the eighty thousand crowns and the land she believed she was owed by her later brother, Edward.

But when would that be? With no help from Ireland or France it looked as though Perkin's position was weakening.

Suddenly the situation changed. News was received from England that King Henry had left London to visit Lancashire where his mother was ill. This might be the moment for Perkin to act, strike against England itself! Yes, it was time – though he knew that if he failed, there could only be one outcome: the penalty for treason was only too well known.

CHAPTER 4

July 1495. While King Henry was still up in the north, Duchess Margaret and Archduke Maximilian provided Perkin with fourteen ships and nearly three hundred men for the invasion of England. These men were a rough old bunch. Some of them had been serving gaol sentences for robbery and brawling in the street. By volunteering they had got their freedom.

Time was of the essence for who knew how long King Henry would be away in Lancashire. Battle equipment had to be loaded aboard quickly – swords, lances, pikes, crossbows and arrows.

At dawn the ships slipped silently out of port into the open sea, heading away from Flanders and over to Kent. Perkin could feel the pouch that contained copies of his agreement with the Duchess. It was safely attached to his belt and was a constant reminder of all the Duchess had done for him – the introductions to the great courts of Europe, the money spent on his behalf and now the ships for his crossing to England. He owed everything to her. When he became King of England, and was betrothed to a beautiful princess and held his own grand court in London, he would repay the Duchess with the money and land he had promised, and more besides. For the moment Perkin was confident of a warm welcome to England, one of his sailors having told him that Kentishmen were always ripe for rebellion against unpopular kings. And Henry was an unpopular king.

The coast of Flanders was disappearing into the distance. As the sun came up it seemed to herald a bright day and a glorious one. Shortly after midday they caught sight of the white cliffs of Dover glistening in the sunlight. But it was too difficult to make a landing there, so they ventured further along the coast.

Soon they saw the fishing village of Deal. This looked more promising: the beach was deserted and the land was flat. Waves roared and crashed onto the stones, and jets of cold white spray shot into the air with a great hiss. Overhead, the clouds were becoming darker. Gulls squawked, circled and dived down for fish.

Beneath them, shafts of light gleamed on the water, revealing traces of broken fishermen's nets and brown slimy seaweed.

Suddenly one of the English sailors caught sight of a small band of men approaching. 'We're the Duke of York's men!' he yelled across.

A great cheer went up from the locals and they started to come right down to the water's edge. Another great cheer. The men of Deal beckoned vigorously for them to come ashore. About half of Perkin's men did so.

In their enthusiasm to get ashore, several men mistook the depth of the water, which was about twelve feet. Most managed to stagger to the beach but some had to be rescued. It was an unpromising start.

From his post aboard ship, Perkin watched the Kentish men drag a barrel down the pebbles towards their guests. As the top was levered off, whoops of delight went up. It must be ale! Perkin's men were now sitting down; some wrestled playfully on the beach. The atmosphere was relaxed and every so often peels of laughter rang out. As Perkin's men became drunk, some of the Kentish men went off to fetch more barrels from the nearest alehouse.

Suddenly, one of the sailors high above in the

rigging gave a shout: 'Henry's soldiers!'

'The enemy!' yelled another.

To think that they had been so easily tricked. The local men had had no intention of going to fetch more ale. Now that they had succeeded in getting Perkin's men drunk, they had gone off to find the Mayor of Sandwich! And here the Mayor was, bold as brass – with some two hundred armed men into the bargain.

What could Perkin's men do? Not a lot, seeing as all their pikes and crossbows were still stowed in the holds of the ships. It would have taken ages to get them all out, and the men were too drunk to use them anyway.

Without time even to put their armour back on, grabbing whatever weapon they could, the men staggered around on the pebbles, trying to put up a fight. At this point, Perkin waded in himself, but a glancing blow from an enemy sword badly pierced his upper arm.

He ripped off a piece of his shirt and pressed it against the wound to stop the bleeding as best he could but the pain shot up and down his arm. Ale might have helped ease the pain but it had all been drunk.

He did his best to oversee the fighting but it was hopeless. Their superior numbers and better weapons gave the Kentishmen too great an advantage. And within the hour Perkin was forced to retreat to his ship, pull up anchor and set sail.

One hundred and sixty-nine of Perkin's men were taken prisoner and dragged along the road to Sandwich, their backs bleeding horribly. Most ended up being hanged at the Tyburn gallows in London. A wretched few were taken from Tyburn all the way back to the coast again, where their bodies were strung up and left to swing in the sea breezes along the shore of Kent as a terrible warning to others that might chance their luck invading.

CHAPTER 5

Early the next day, after an anxious return sea cross-ing, Perkin's men anchored off the French coast. Perkin's immediate concern was to beat a retreat to Flanders, to the Duchess's court – and safety.

Leaving his ship in the hands of his loyal crew, he bade them farewell and, putting on a brave face, set off on foot for the village of Dunkerque. Here he was able to buy a horse, and after three days' solid riding he arrived back at Malines. However, when he reached the court he found that the Duchess was away on business. His spirits were already at a low ebb; now he became frustrated and angry, too. Why wasn't she there when he needed her? For an instant he even considered pack-ing everything in and returning to his family in Tournai.

However, when Perkin calmed down he began to

reason things through. Why should the Duchess have expected him back so soon? After all, if everything had gone to plan, he ought at that very moment to be entering London, ready to be crowned King of England. He knew that despite this setback he could go on to fulfil this ambition even now, live this dream, and stay loyal to the Duchess. But without her there to guide and advise Perkin the initiative now lay with him. Ideas started to float into his head. Suppose he raised recruits in Flanders and headed for Ireland, built up a great army there, and then crossed to England – to Cornwall where the people so hated Henry that they wanted to break away from England altogether. The excitement of even thinking about it gave him fresh hope and sent a sudden rush of colour to Perkin's cheeks.

* * *

Four months later; Stirling Castle, Scotland. An echo of hooves rang out as Perkin's wagon clattered under a gateway and emerged into a courtyard. What had brought him hundreds of miles north to Scotland, further from his homeland than he had ever been before?

After his escape from the disaster at Deal, Perkin had tried again to get help from the lords of Ireland but had failed. He had been about to leave for England when one night, sitting in a tavern in Kinsale deep in the south of Ireland, two men had approached him. They spoke in a curious accent, certainly not Irish: 'Your Grace, our master, King James of Scotland has heard that you carry letters from Archduke Maximilian and the Duchess of Burgundy that prove your identity. Our King would happily welcome you into Scotland and will give you all the honours that are due to you.'

The offer came out of the blue and it put Perkin in a dilemma, he needed time to think. He was reluctant to alter his plan and leave Ireland. But the situation had changed: he had expected the support of the Irish but that support had not been forthcoming. Next he had planned to go to Cornwall – but could he rely on the Cornish to back him? Nothing seemed to be certain in his world any longer.

On the other hand, going to Scotland would bring with it the support of the Scottish King, James IV, an ambitious man with plans to extend his northern lands into England. Furthermore, James's support would bring with it the backing of a powerful army. The down side was that it might delay him reaching London. Perkin weighed up the situation carefully and finally gave the two messengers their answer: he would go with them to Scotland.

And so here he was, in central Scotland, with the November cold biting into his bones as he was led into the palace at Stirling. The Great Hall was full of guests in thick cloaks and gloves. At the far end was a high platform where the King of Scotland was seated.

James rose. He was tall and handsome with long red hair and a ruddy complexion. He greeted Perkin in a confident manner, calling him his 'cousin' and even giving him a little bow. What a contrast James presented to the bumbling King of France – to whom he had admitted that he was an impostor. Perkin looked up to the galleries and with all the confidence and bearing of a prince began his well-practised speech. He talked about how his dying father had given instructions to their Uncle Richard to look after the two princes, but how Richard had ignored them and ordered the poor boys' executions. He explained how his brother Edward had been put to death, and how he had been allowed to escape.

When he had finished there was a burst of applause and courtiers presented him with an emerald green cloak, decorated with a border of white fur. Perkin was delighted.

All the while, there was a knowing expression on

the King's face. Perkin felt that somehow the King did not fully believe him. Perhaps the rumours that he was an impostor had worked their way this far north. But did it really matter as long as he promised his support?

In fact the two became good friends. Many events were put on in Perkin's honour — Highland games, football and jousting, where knights on horseback would ride towards each other and try to knock each other off their horse with their lances.

One evening after dinner James brought up the subject of marriage. Although James himself was not yet married, he strongly believed that every king should get a wife at the earliest opportunity, so as to provide strong sons. And Perkin, who was now twenty-one years old, needed to start thinking about such things.

'I must introduce you to the Earl of Huntly's daughter, young Katherine Gordon,' said James with a broad smile. 'My own cousin! By my troth, I think she would suit you admirably well.'

Perkin asked the steward to find out more about the Lady Katherine; and the next day he reported back that she was everything the King had said she was — a lovely girl with long, flowing chestnut hair, hazel eyes and a beautiful complexion. That she also had his own dear mother's name, Katherine, warmed Perkin to her even more, and made him think that it was a sign of their entwined destinies.

* * *

The gleaming doors of the King's apartment slowly opened, as if by their own accord, to reveal the Earl of Huntly and his wife. For a moment the Earl's thick grey winter cloak obscured the slim young woman behind him but she now followed her parents nervously into the room. Perkin was transfixed. Her complexion was fairer than that of any girl he had ever seen before, beautiful and milky white, and her hair flowed down her back like a stream of spun silk. What a gem this girl was, so lovely, so pure.

The King made the introductions. Katherine made a curtsey. Her wide hazel eyes shone up at him. 'I'm very pleased to meet you, Prince Richard.'

That evening the young couple were placed next to one another at dinner. From time to time they caught each other's eye; but the conversations all around them were so noisy that when they tried to speak they could hardly make themselves heard. Both of them found this very amusing and started to laugh. Katherine had a wonderful laugh, a light playful laugh that sent a tingle of happiness down Perkin's spine.

* * *

From that moment they saw each other every day. If the weather permitted, they went hunting for hare and deer with the King, or strolled in the palace gardens. On wet days they would walk in the Long Gallery and Perkin would tell her about his plans.

Katherine was thrilled to hear the names of the places he had been to, and of those he promised to take her to. It was clear that he was a wronged man who was determined to set things right, to fight for justice. And she loved him for it.

One day as they sat on the banks of a loch they kissed for the first time. Perkin told her that he loved her, that if she agreed to become his wife he would share with her the glory that he hoped to achieve in his life.

* * *

Throughout the twilight days of December and January, preparations were completed for their wedding. As the first few light snowflakes of winter fell, invitations were sent to the leading noble families. Cooks and wine merchants took orders for the wedding banquet. Extra seamstresses were brought in to take measurements for the wedding gowns. Bright new tapestries appeared in the bedrooms and carpets were laid over the rushes on the floor of the Great Hall.

The wedding day arrived. Perkin wore the special emerald green cloak presented to him on the day of his arrival. Kate wore her hair long and loose as a sign of her maidenhood, and on her head she wore a garland of wild flowers. She was dressed in a high-waisted, wide-sleeved gown made from blue velvet, with trimmings of fur.

Outside the chapel door they made their vows to one another. Perkin handed Kate a gold ring and a gift of gold coins wrapped in white linen. Side by side they walked into the chapel for the wedding mass. Everywhere was decorated in scarlet and gold. Big bunches of mistletoe and holly had been placed all around, their bright berries glowing like lamps in the half-light. After a short ceremony the priest stretched cloth of gold over them. And so they were married.

When they returned to the palace it was time for the banqueting to begin. Cooks bustled in and out, carrying silver dishes of fresh salmon and trout. Two kitchen boys carried in a great boar's head on a huge silver platter, and soon a rich assortment of roast meats and fowl lay alongside it — venison, pork, lamb and chicken. Underneath the tables, dogs were already roaming freely, hoping that one of the guests would throw them a juicy bone.

The high table at the end of the hall had been covered in purple, black and gold; the dishes were made not just from silver but from gold, too. Kate and Perkin were placed to the right of the King. As they ate and drank in the flickering shadows of the hall, a dwarf and jesters moved in between the tables performing tricks.

As the evening wore on and the guests became louder, Kate was led away by her maidservant and the priest. He had to bless the marriage bed so they would have strong healthy sons.

* * *

Several months passed until one spring morning King James summoned Perkin to his private chamber. Perkin crossed the Great Hall where a feast had been the night before. The place stank of sweat, smoke and damp clothes, and he was forced to step over a puddle of vomit.

The King was seated at his table working on some documents. When he spoke, his tone was grave: 'King Henry has offered me his daughter, the Princess Margaret, as my bride. She is very young, only six years old but if I were betrothed to her it would mean a lasting peace with England. Only there is one condition to the betrothal – that I should give you up.'

Perkin was astonished.

'His ally King Charles of France has also promised me one hundred thousand crowns.'

But James was teasing him. He put a friendly hand on his shoulder. 'Don't worry. I've no intention of giving you up. We shall be going into battle against England as planned. All I ask for is that when you become King of England you give me back the town of Berwick-upon-Tweed. The town lies on the border between England and Scotland, and is really mine in any case… Oh yes, and fifty thousand marks in money,' he added, rolling up the documents.

Kate begged Perkin to let her accompany him to war. But Perkin stood firm. 'It won't be a long campaign. I'll return to fetch you. You'll come with me to London as my queen.'

Over the next six months, more than fourteen hundred men were mustered – all Scottish outlaws and soldiers, hired from overseas. To these, King James added all the forces he could from Scotland. The royal armourer in Edinburgh sent a supply of arrows to Stirling; and new doublets, cloaks and thick winter stockings were made. Perkin was given a luxurious carriage so that he could go to war in style and a special banner of red and blue taffeta with his own coat of arms on it.

In September 1496, with drummers beating out a marching step, the army set off towards Berwick, carrying tents, guns and ammunition. At the head of the army was a herald with a trumpet, ready to proclaim Perkin King Richard IV of England, and call upon every Englishmen to take up weapons to fight on his behalf.

But the results were disappointing. Although they managed to raid the valleys of the Tweed and Till and demolish a few castle towers, the northern lords whom Perkin had hoped would support him stayed loyal to King Henry.

Besides, King Henry's spies had already sent word to their master that an attack from Scotland was imminent, and Henry had ordered an English army to head north from Newcastle to confront the Scots. When this news reached King James he was forced to withdraw.

On his return to Stirling, James told Perkin: 'I have done all I can to restore you to the English throne. Sadly, you did not find among the English the friendship and support you had expected. I can provide you with ships but can do no more. I wish you well. I fear you must continue alone.'

* * *

Perkin knew that it was pointless to stay on. His hopes were now pinned on the people in the south-west of England. This time, though, he must keep his plans secret from King Henry's spies.

'It is a mad scheme,' Kate declared, as she sat brushing her hair. 'What makes you think men in Cornwall are going to help you any more than those in the north of England?'

'They'll support me. I told you how angry they are about having to pay taxes for Henry's Scottish war.'

'But what can you offer them for their support?'

'I'll see that they get their reward.'

Kate had no choice but to give in, and they set off for the port of Ayr. Perkin was eager to inspect the four ships that he had been promised for the journey to Cornwall. But they were nowhere near ready. As for the sailors, they looked very rough types. This uncertainty made Kate even more anxious. 'The men admit they have never undertaken such a long journey before. They are just local sailors and fishermen. I have an awful premonition that something terrible is going to happen to us!'

CHAPTER 6

15th July, St Swithin's Day, dawned cool and breezy. Grey skies loomed overhead. The local astrologer had advised Perkin and his men that this would be the best day to sail. But it looked like rain, and they all knew what that would mean – continuous rain for forty days and forty nights.

The *Cuckoo*, a small sailing ship that James had provided, was moored at the quayside where some of the locals from Ayr were gathered to wish Perkin and Kate well on their voyage to Cornwall. Fishermen looked up from mending their nets to watch them sail out of the harbour. Perkin had not realised how cramped it would be until they got on board. The masts and the rigging seemed to take up most of the deck. Below, in their cabin, he soon realised that most sailors must be short men, as he kept banging his head against the beams.

As so often in those days, the weather dictated the course of events. There were no meteorological reports to help sailors predict rain and storms, and ships without today's navigation equipment were very vulnerable.

On the first day at sea the weather turned foul, the sails made a cracking sound in the wind and the *Cuckoo* started to roll. Some sailors muttered about the terrible whirlpools at sea that could suck in ships and smash them to bits. Perkin already knew of the tales of a sea-monster called the kraken with jaws big enough to hold a man and a horse, and teeth so sharp it could crunch bones into tiny pieces. He told himself he did not believe in such a creature.

With the weather in such a threatening mood, the captain told Perkin that he would have to change his plans and head for the coast of Ireland. Cornwall would have to wait. Perkin had no choice but to agree.

* * *

They left the next morning and headed south towards the tip of Ireland, hoping to reach Kinsale. The sea was calmer, but still they were shrouded in mist.

Suddenly they saw the sails and masts of three approaching ships. The cry went up among the sailors:

'It's the Spanish!' Even as Perkin heard the shouts of alarm, one of the ships, a merchant ship, drew alongside. Before they knew it, some Spaniards had climbed aboard the *Cuckoo*. Their short swords held Perkin's crew at bay.

Perkin himself was quickly seized by three of the Spaniards. They lunged forward, flinging him against the side, pinning his arms behind him. The roughest looking of the three held the blade of his sword at Perkin's throat. Perkin's knowledge of Spanish was poor but even he could understand the few words that were said – that he was their prisoner and they were going to take him back to Spain.

Perkin was desperate. What could he do? Money! That was the only thing that men like this understood. Haltingly, in Spanish, he tried to explain. He would pay them three thousand silver nobles – a huge sum to such men – if they allowed the *Cuckoo* to continue on its way to Cornwall. He would give them the money when they arrived.

The three Spaniards exchanged a few words and nodded in agreement. Perkin breathed a sigh of relief.

Thus they sailed due south, heading towards Land's End, the last stage of their journey.

* * *

But just as Perkin thought their problems were over, another disaster struck. On the horizon they could see a small fleet of warships. Were they friendly? Perkin was soon to find out.

One of Perkin's men high above in the crow's nest shouted out, 'KING HENRY'S SHIPS!'

What should they do? What could they do? They could try to run for Ireland but they would probably never make it. The King's ships were big and sturdy and swift under sail. Perkin's thoughts raced ahead. They were after *him*. He was the prize. Could he perhaps conceal himself in the ship and escape capture? If Henry's men did not find him on board, they might just let the ship move on. And what about his wife, and Jane, her maid? He remembered that he had seen some empty barrels below deck. He threw himself down the steps to where Kate and Jane had been waiting in their cabin. Quickly he explained his plan to them. What choice did they have?

The captain came down the ladder and Perkin explained his idea as well as he could. The captain nod-ded and pointed to three barrels at the very back. They stank with the remains of sour wine. Perkin helped Kate into one barrel, the maid into the second, and then he climbed into a third. The captain nailed down the lids. Perkin whispered to Kate 'Be still, my dear! Don't make a sound!'

Perkin fought back his rising panic. Would they be able to breathe in the barrels? Gradually, as his eyes grew accustomed to the dark, he realised he could see tiny chinks of light through the wood. They wouldn't suffocate after all.

But there were other problems. He could not straighten his back, his neck and head were twisted. The smell of stinking wine was so bad that he feared he would be sick.

Suddenly, the ship juddered. Perkin's barrel began to lurch. At any moment it would surely overturn. One of the English ships must have come alongside by now. Yes, some of King Henry's men had boarded. He could hear the sound of muffled shouting overhead. There were

English voices. Henry's men were obviously not happy with the answers they were getting. A thud of heavy footsteps overhead.

The ship was starting to rock in the wind. The barrels were beginning to sway and tilt, Perkin felt giddy.

Suddenly there was silence. The men must have gone: had Perkin's crew managed to deceive them and send them on their way? Perkin waited, full of anxiety. Each second now felt like a minute, an hour. Nothing. Where was the captain? Why wasn't he releasing them? How was Kate?

Then at last he heard boots coming down the ladder. To his horror the voices were English ones. Clearly, the King's men had not been so easily dismissed. Now they were going to search below. MY GOD! They would find him!

Perkin felt as though he was about to faint. A dull ache stretched across his forehead. He felt hot. His chest began to tighten. On top of everything else he felt something slippery wriggle across his hand. He shuddered. He must be strong. He couldn't be the one to let them all down.

Suddenly, there was a wrenching sound, timber smashing to pieces. Shouts of anger and confusion. Sailors' curses. Scrambling on the decks above. Could the ships be sinking? What was happening? Perkin was terrified that they were all going to drown. Were they ever going to see the light of day again? Or would the barrels be their final resting-place?

Even as these thoughts spun round in his head, the ship lurched violently and began to roll. More noise. Movement. Footsteps approaching. Perkin did not know what to expect. Was it the captain come to free them? Or had Henry's men forced the Spanish to tell them he was hiding on board?

In an instant, the lid of his barrel was wrenched off. He looked up but the shock of the light made it difficult for him to see anything. Gradually he made out a familiar face looking down at him. It was the Spanish captain.

Trembling, Perkin was helped out of the barrel. He could not be sure that the danger was over. Perhaps Henry's men were still on board, and had forced the Spanish crew to fetch them up on deck. His knees buckled beneath him and he fell to the floor. The captain hauled him to his feet and slapped him on the back. To his enormous relief Perkin realised that he was safe! The captain told him that the ship had broken free from the English in the storm and they were now flying before the wind, bound for Cornwall.

Perkin turned to the other two barrels and started to pull at the lids but made a poor job of it. The captain pushed him aside and quickly levered them off. Kate seemed half-conscious, lying curled up inside the barrel. The two men gently lifted her out and placed her on the floor. Perkin knelt beside Kate and held her closely, reassuring her that they were safe. Jane, who was made of sterner stuff, crawled over to her mistress and started to wipe her face. 'Sir, my mistress needs water!'

Perkin nodded and stumbled towards the ladder. As he climbed up onto the deck, he felt the hail stones against his face. What a blessed relief! He breathed deeply as the wind cut across his body. He turned to the captain. 'Why didn't you give us up?,' asked Perkin in his rough Spanish. 'Surely they must have offered you a reward?' The captain grinned, showing a mouthful of black teeth. 'Oh yes, they offered a reward all right, but only two thousand nobles. You'll be paying me three thousand when we reach Cornwall! Or else…'

He drew his hand across his throat. Perkin only hoped the Cornish rebels would keep their promise to help him, otherwise the captain's threat would be all too real.

CHAPTER 7

The coast appeared in the distance like the steps of a giant's staircase. Sunlight glistened on the waves. A lone seagull screeched above.

To Perkin's great relief, a messenger (a spy) was waiting for him on the shore, with money from the Duchess Margaret. He would now be able to pay the Spanish captain what he owed. As the three weary travellers waded ashore, their feet sank into shimmering white sand, England's shores, his kingdom. He picked up a handful of sand and let it trickle through his fingers.

Fishermen drifted down the winding paths to the shore but were reluctant to come too close. Perkin told them not to be afraid, that he was their true king and promised them money if they helped him. They warmed to this, and one offered to take them in his cart to the nearest town, Penzance.

In the fish market there Perkin proclaimed himself king and recruited nearly two thousand men into his army. Some of these men had friends who, a few months earlier, had marched on London, complaining about King Henry's war taxes. Henry's spearmen had butchered them just south of London at Blackheath. By joining Perkin's army, these new recruits would try to avenge their friends' terrible deaths.

'Sir!' A man with a bushy black beard stepped forward. 'If you are looking for someone who knows the area well, please look no further. Nicholas Astley's your man! I can guide you to Exeter and beyond. I can also read and write, sir.'

'You can write?' asked Perkin.

'Why yes, I have just copied out a long list of Cornishmen. Refused to pay their taxes, every one of them! And my name heads the list...'

With that, a stocky man butted in: 'Sir, a merchant just arrived from Exeter reports that King Henry knows of your landing and is assembling an army against you even as we speak.'

'How long will it take the King's army to reach us?'

'His army travels fast, sir, and may be facing us at

Exeter. You must see to the safety of your wife. You dare not let her accompany you to London. It is too risky.'

'Risky? In what way?'

'Being captured, sir. She must be left in a safe place. Not far from here is a little island just off the coast, locally known by the name of St Michael's Mount. When the tide is high it is cut off and completely isolated. Your wife will be safe there. The monks will give her refuge.'

* * *

The Mount lay at a short distance out to sea – a pyramid of rock bathed in bright sunlight. Some fishermen lent them a boat and they crossed to the island, mooring it at a jetty. They passed some cottages and monastery buildings, then followed the Cornishmen up a steep rocky path until the castle entrance with its half-raised portcullis came into sight.

A group of monks dressed in black habits welcomed them and led them up a short flight of steps and through a low doorway. The door closed behind them with a thud and bolts were drawn across.

Kate and Jane were entrusted to the care of the monks who showed them their sleeping quarters high up in one of the towers. As the women disappeared up a spiral staircase, Perkin stayed behind looking out to sea, deep in contemplation. He was on the threshold of the final stage of his enterprise – the journey to London where he would be crowned King of England. Sadly, for that last part he and his wife were to be separated.

By the time they were ready to leave, the tide was out and Perkin crossed the stone causeway to the mainland on foot. Overhead the clouds were patchy – it looked like rain. He turned around. High above, from a solitary grey tower, he thought he could see the silhouette of a figure waving at him.

* * *

As Perkin began the march eastwards towards Bodmin, hundreds more men from the surrounding villages joined his army – fishermen and tin-miners, farmers and peasants. The oldest may have been 50 – he was not sure, because people seldom recorded or even knew their dates of birth. The youngest was just 12, a bright, fresh-skinned boy, eager to fight. All they had to fight with were scythes and sticks. Some had nothing at all, and made do with splinters of wood, nails and stones they picked up from the fields. What they had in common was a deep hatred of Henry's taxes.

'Why should we pay for the King's damned wars up in Scotland?' said one of them.

'Yeah! What's the King ever done to help us?' asked his mate.

'Not a damn thing! We must stand firm and fight the swine!'

Perkin did all he could to train these men and get them to listen and obey instructions but it was a hopeless task. They preferred to spend their time drinking, gambling and telling one another dirty stories.

In the square at Bodmin, Perkin was proclaimed King Richard IV of England, and was soon joined by nearly a thousand more men, making his army about six thousand in all.

Despite the unruliness of the rabble, all seemed to be going well, when suddenly bad news arrived from a cloth merchant who had travelled the road between Exeter and Bodmin. The King's army — some fifteen hundred well-armed men, led by the Earl of Devon — was heading their way.

As Perkin's men prepared to cross Bodmin Moor, the Cornishmen warned them to take care for there were bogs deep enough to drag down a man and his horse. At length they descended through a steep, dark wood, crossed by dozens of bubbling streams.

The next day they reached the River Tamar that separates the great western counties of Cornwall and Devon, and counted themselves lucky not to see the Earl of Devon and his men lined up on the opposite bank. It turned out that he had come the day before but had withdrawn when he had heard about the size of Perkin's army. But Perkin knew he did not have long: the Earl would have gone for reinforcements. The King's army would be back.

* * *

Three days later Perkin and the Cornishmen approached Exeter. The air was full of the smoke of wood fires and burning pitch. It was almost midnight, and every gate along the city wall was closed and bolted for the night. Outside one gate there were buckets of urine, left by the inhabitants to be collected by local tanners who used the ammonia to soften the leather.

Two guards patrolling the wall went off to wake the mayor and city aldermen. They came with torches blazing in the breeze, but when they spoke they said they were too afraid of Henry to join the fight; they were weary of marches and battles, and wanted to stay with their families. If they had to fight it would be to protect their city from Perkin's army!

When he heard that, Perkin threw a spear at the North Gate as a sign that his men intended to take the city by force. He ordered five oak trees to be felled and used as battering rams. Some men were set to scale the walls, others to burn down the North Gate. It was a daunting challenge, as it was protected by a strong gateway and a 'killing ground' – a yard surrounded by arrow slits and cannon. Mind you, for men like his who had been drinking since the light of day, anything may have seemed possible.

The drawbridge was raised, so the only means of reaching the keep was across the moat, even though that was filled with stinking sewage from the castle toilets. As they waded across, boulders, boiling water and dead animals were thrown down on them.

One of Perkin's men was half way up the wall when a cauldron of burning pitch was thrown down on him.

The force of the scalding liquid flung him from the ladder. By the time help arrived, his face was hardly recognisable, his skin bright red, the pitch continuing to burn into his skin and hair, exposing his cheek bones and lower jaw.

At the East Gate things were going better, and at last Perkin's men forced an entry with their battering rams. A frantic hand-to-hand encounter began with clubs, scythes – even bare fists – and for a while it looked as though the men of Exeter were going to yield to his superior numbers.

But it was not to be. At that critical moment the Earl of Devon arrived, supported by fifteen hundred fresh recruits, and terrible fighting took place. The injuries were fearful – severed limbs, crushed bones – and most injuries were on Perkin's side. In the enemy camp, army surgeons dipped the stumps of legs in scalding hot oil and clamped red-hot irons on to gaping wounds in a desperate attempt to stop the bleeding.

They fought on as best they could in the night drizzle, tripping and stumbling over the dead bodies of their men, and many more who were not yet dead. Conditions were impossible, and soon after midnight Perkin agreed to a truce. The rules said that all activity had to stop, defences could not be improved and no cannon could be moved around. The siege would continue in the morning. In the meantime Perkin withdrew to spend the night at a village nearby.

The next morning, as he rode into the still smoky city, Perkin was in for a shock. The defenders had broken the rules and moved a massive cannon into place. The Cornishmen looked at each other in desperation.

'We'll piss on their gunpowder and set fire to their buildings,' said one of them.

But Perkin knew that their situation was already hopeless. A number of his men who came from Devon were already beginning to drift back to their homes, tired and demoralised.

Then came the body blow: they heard that a second division of the King's men was closing in on the city. Perkin looked up to the cannon directed at them from the walls; and that single glance was enough. His only option now was to head directly for Taunton, some forty miles away. The town would not be easy to capture but at least Perkin would be one step nearer to London.

CHAPTER 8

Taunton, Somerset – 19 September 1497. A great clattering of hooves as horses galloped into the square. HENRY'S MEN! A stout, fierce-looking man dismounted and introduced himself to Perkin as the King's Lord Chamberlain. 'Sir, I come with a promise from the King that you shall be pardoned if you lay down your arms.'

'Do you really believe I have come this far only to give in?' Perkin retorted. 'Give up my inheritance? I have the backing of the courts of Europe and the King of Scotland.'

A great cheer went up from the people of Taunton.

As Henry's envoy rode away, Perkin felt relieved that he had managed to mask his fears and anxieties. For the truth was that his heart had failed when he had seen the royal standard fluttering in the breeze. The only way to save his own skin was to escape to the Duchess's court in Flanders.

So, at midnight when most of his men were sound asleep, Perkin passed word to sixty horsemen to get ready. Quickly they fastened their spurs and left the camp, bound for Southampton Water. It was a foul autumn night to be out riding. There seemed to be no end to the stinging, cold rain. Perkin's cloak felt icy against his skin.

As it started to grow light, two horsemen whom Perkin had sent ahead returned with news that the King had set up a blockade along the coast. Only yesterday Perkin had had dreams of conquering Exeter and then riding victoriously to London to claim the throne. Now he stood no chance even of reaching Flanders!

'Right, we'd better head for Beaulieu,' said a merchant who had joined Perkin's men at Taunton. 'It's a sanctuary.'

'A sanctuary?'

'Yes. It's a place over which the King has no control, sir. I know the abbot at Beaulieu well.'

'Where is this place?'

'It lies on the edge of the New Forest in the county of Hampshire.'

*   *   *

Beaulieu Abbey seemed a peaceful spot. Surrounding it were fields of sheep that supplied the abbey with wool and skin for making hoods and parchment. When the porter who opened the gate saw their drenched and dishevelled clothes, he mistook Perkin and his companions for poor people, begging for food and clothing. But as soon as Abbot Humphrey set eyes on his friend, the merchant, they were welcomed inside.

The abbot immediately made them surrender their weapons, such as they had – a few clubs and knives. In return for these, he promised to feed and protect them.

The next afternoon, as light was beginning to fade, word came that the King's forces had been sighted.

'Damn. We've had it now!' said Perkin.

'Not at all, sir,' replied the merchant. 'This is a sanctuary. We are safe.'

'But for how long?'

'Sanctuary in a church guarantees immunity from arrest for a week…'

'A week!'

'Please, sir, let me finish,' continued the merchant. 'Such is the case for churches. In abbeys, however, particularly one such as Beaulieu with special holy relics, we shall be safe for a month at least.'

'But suppose Henry never gives up?' Perkin persisted.

'Look! Do you see those stones over there in the distance? There are stones all around the abbey like that. As long as we stay inside the stones, we're safe from our enemies.'

'And what if they take no notice of those stones?'

'They wouldn't dare! Their souls would rot in hell.'

* * *

True to form, the King did begin to grow weary from waiting, and eventually sent out a herald to offer Perkin a free pardon, provided that he accompanied him to Taunton, withdrew his claim to the throne of England and owned up to his true origins.

Perkin could never have hoped for more generous terms. No action would be taken against him. What other choice had he, anyway? It seemed he had nothing to lose. He gave himself up.

As he was travelling to Taunton, the heavy rain of the past few days began to ease, only for the sky to darken again. It looked as though a storm was brewing. Grey clouds swirled over the Blackdown Hills. The trees swayed in the wind, their tops sweeping into one another as if they were sharing a secret.

Perkin and his guards stopped overnight at an inn. It gave him a chance to dictate his confession to his friend Nicholas Astley, the scribe from Penzance. It would need to be ready for Perkin to read out when he arrived in Taunton. The innkeeper, a jolly man with a blotchy red face, provided parchment, a quill and some black ink. Perkin watched Astley make strokes in his clear and elegant hand.

The following morning the weather had cleared and they continued their journey. It was market day, and the centre of Taunton was full of stalls and tradesmen, who called out their wares in a rich accent – butter and corn, lace and velvet. They entered the market. A platform had been built out of beer barrels and planks of wood. Several important-looking officials in scarlet robes hovered around it.

At first Perkin could not see the King at all. Then Henry's cup-bearer moved aside and he caught a glimpse of the grandest man in England – a surprisingly small figure, weighed down by his heavy armour.

Suddenly, the King looked up and fixed his dark eyes directly on Perkin. When he spoke, his tone was solemn: 'Sir, you have been brought here to account for your misdeeds and to repent. Many a prince would have executed you at once... but I am known for my mercy. I am willing to offer you terms. If you confess and admit your true identity, you will be granted a free pardon.'

There was a pause.

'I await your reply, sir.'

Perkin reached for the roll of paper on which Astley had recorded his confession the night before. The King's eyes remained fixed on him, cold as stone.

'I want it to be known that I was not born in England...' Perkin began, now filled with doubt. 'I, I... was born in Tournai in Flanders. My father was John Warbeck, a customs officer. It all began when the Duchess of Burgundy sent me to Ireland. The inhabitants of Cork mistook me for the Duke of York. They said they would help me to become King of England. I agreed – I dared not go against their wishes for my own safety. So they taught me what I needed to know and what I should say. Before I knew it, the French King was inviting me to his court in Paris. Next, I found myself in Scotland – married to King James's own cousin.'

The King averted his gaze. His hand tightened on his sword. The tone of his voice was severe. 'Now, at last, we all know the truth!'

He turned to the captain of the guard: 'Ride to St Michael's Mount! Seize the Lady Katherine Gordon and bring her to Exeter!'

Perkin hardly had time to worry about Katherine before the King's guards closed in on him once more. As he left Taunton he was jeered at. Someone in the crowd threw an apple core that clipped him on the cheek.

'Lying bastard!' yelled a young man, waving his fist.

'Traitor!' shouted another.

Later that day he was taken to Exeter, and there saw the damage that his men had inflicted during their attack – the battered East Gate and the torn up road-way where the terrible slaughter had occurred. Perkin cursed himself for having been tricked into a shabby truce that night, and given the men of Exeter an opportunity to move their cannon in. He thought about what might have been.

Next day in the cathedral precincts, Perkin saw

several of his men being dragged across the mud towards the Treasurer's House in front of which the King sat.

The King rose, and stood with his legs astride, his face a terrifying shade of purple.

'Cornish traitors! You must suffer the penalty you deserve – DEATH!'

The men were dragged away; they included all Perkin's friends and advisers.

The guards then led Perkin inside the Treasurer's House. It took a while before his eyes became used to the gloom. It was then that he saw Kate. There were dark rings under her eyes. He knew she had been weeping.

She looked straight at him with a cold and bitter stare. There was a stony silence.

'Kate, Kate, will you find it in yourself to forgive me? … I am not who I said I was… I am not King Edward's son.'

Tears welled up in her eyes. When she spoke, her voice was weak and came from far back in her throat: 'You deceived me with your false stories… You lured me from my home, my parents, my friends… how I wish you'd never come to these shores!'

The King tried to comfort her. 'I am very sad it has

come to this. You deserved a far better husband than this scoundrel here. You shall be taken to Westminster and treated kindly.' He beckoned to his servants, who led her away. Perkin, meanwhile, was taken prisoner in the castle.

As darkness descended over Exeter, Perkin could hear the bell-man in the distance. 'Look well to your locks,' the bell-man shouted as he signalled an end to another day.

Tomorrow Perkin would be taken to London. There was no knowing what would await him there.

CHAPTER 9

From Exeter all the way to London, Kate was kept a good distance behind Perkin, and when they stopped for a change of horses or to spend the night they were forbidden to speak to one another. On reaching London, they would go their separate ways. Kate would be taken to the Palace of Westminster. Perkin would be imprisoned in the Tower. No more safe sanctuaries for him. The game was up. He would be locked away, just like the boy whom he had been impersonating for the past thirteen years.

* * *

Towards the end of the fourth day of travel, the dismal party crossed London Bridge. Before them, shrouded in the late afternoon mist, stood the grim outlines of the Tower. They followed the moat for a while, then crossed a drawbridge. An iron-studded door was drawn back for them, and they passed under an arch with a portcullis. In the distance, the rhythmical blows of a hammer signalled that a scaffold was being prepared for the execution of a traitor. Perkin was put in a cell high up in a tower in the south-east corner. Its rough grey walls were carved with graffiti made by earlier prisoners as they had awaited their fate.

The following day Perkin was taken to the council chamber in the White Tower to be questioned by three inquisitors. 'Why didn't you refuse to take part in their schemes?' they asked him. 'You must have known that by agreeing you were being disloyal, committing treason.'

'I had no choice,' Perkin replied. 'I dared not disobey.'

After another grilling two days later, the inquisitors pronounced themselves satisfied that he had told them the truth. 'You will be taken to the Palace of Westminster. You will be able to move around at will there. You will be free to see your wife during the daylight hours.'

A reprieve... of sorts! Perkin could not have wished for more. But his meeting with his wife later that day turned out to be a very unhappy affair. Feelings of betrayal showed in Kate's strained face. 'You tricked me!' she cried. 'You have destroyed me. Get out of my sight. I don't wish to see you ever again!'

* * *

June 1499. Time was slipping away. Perkin knew that somehow he had to escape, and return to Flanders. One night he knotted a couple of sheets together to make a rope, and lowered it from his window. Taking with him the few silver coins he had left, he eased his way down the jagged stone wall, then jumped the rest of the distance, falling without injury onto the grass at the base of the wall. Freedom! He got up and stumbled away into the dark of the night.

Through the little lanes he ran. In his haste he knocked against stalls and stabbed his toe on a beer barrel. At one point a cat squealed as it shot out across his path. In places the lanes were slippery with horse manure and the remains of rotten fruit and vegetables. All there was to guide him was the disgusting smell rising from the Thames, more putrid than ever on that warm summer's night. But the river was also his lifeline to safety – he hoped he would be able to persuade a ship's captain to take him to Flanders.

As Londoners slept in their beds, Perkin picked his way through the silent alleyways to the water's edge. As he neared Alderman's Stairs he moved more cautiously, fearing that he might be recognized. But not a soul was around, nor were any ships moored along that stretch of the river – let alone a vessel to take him to Flanders. He would need to change his plans.

He had learnt during his stay at the Palace of Westminster that the nearest sanctuary was at Sheen near Richmond. Having already been saved from the King's forces once by sanctuary at Beaulieu, he knew this was his only hope now. At Sheen he would have time to plan his escape to Flanders.

He followed the course of the river until he reached Putney, where he asked an old waterman to take him the rest of the way to Richmond. The man grumbled. He was only used to ferrying people across the river. Besides, it was very late. But when Perkin produced a few coins he agreed. The old waterman rowed slowly, cutting his oars deep into the murky water. The stench was overwhelming.

As they neared Richmond it was starting to grow light. Perkin scrambled ashore and made for the safety of the House of Sheen where the Prior offered him refuge for a week.

But somehow or other King Henry got wind of Perkin's hiding place. The King was losing his patience with the benefits of sanctuary, and before the week was out he sent his men into the House of Sheen to drag Perkin back to London under armed escort.

Outside Westminster Hall, his legs were squeezed into a set of stocks and the crossbar clamped down and locked. The stocks had been placed high up on a scaffold constructed from empty wine barrels. Perkin had escaped from King Henry's men on a Spanish ship in barrels similar to these. By a twist of fate he was now being imprisoned by them.

The following day he was taken to Cheapside, placed in a new set of stocks, and again made to repeat his confession. But, as soon as he began reading, he realised that the confession that his friend Nicholas Astley had helped him prepare on his way to Taunton had been altered. It said hardly anything about the support that Perkin had received from King Henry's subjects and laid the blame squarely on Perkin himself. For five hours, crowds of people milled around him, taunting him, calling him lowborn foreign scum.

Afterwards he was taken back to his cell in the Wakefield Tower. The cell had no window, for the guards' instructions were that Perkin was 'to see neither sun nor moon'.

However, by a brilliant stroke of good fortune, the

cell directly above Perkin's turned out to be home to none other than the Earl of Warwick. Being the nephew of the last two Kings of England, Warwick's claim to the throne was far better than King Henry's, in fact second only to that of Prince Richard (Perkin) himself. Warwick, on learning that Perkin had been incarcerated below him, began to knock on the floor of the cell and call down to him.

Next day the knock came again. How was it that it sounded so close? As Perkin looked up he saw a small hole in the corner of the ceiling.

'Perkin, cheer up!' he heard the voice of Warwick's cellmate, Robert Cleymond, calling to him. 'I have just received a letter from a clerk working for the Duchess Margaret. He has been ordered to help you raise an army against Henry!'

Next morning, another voice – not Cleymond's whine, but the mellower, educated tones of the Earl of Warwick himself. 'Cleymond knows a fellow here in the Tower…'

'Can he fix up some disguise for us; get us smuggled out?'

'No, that kind of stuff is for cowards!'

'What then?' Perkin was growing impatient.

'Four guards are involved,' the Earl replied.

'Tomorrow night after the great supper, when all the officers have retired to their chambers – drunk most probably – the guards will go to the Constable's chamber and create a great racket outside. When the Constable opens the door and steps out, they will whack him on the head with their clubs. Then they will release all the prisoners. We shall seize the gunpowder in the Tower, and set it alight. Then, with torches blazing we shall head for Westminster Palace. There, we shall murder Henry, and crown you King Richard IV, King of England.'

Suddenly, Warwick's pace slowed, and he became very serious. 'Perkin. Do you agree to it?'

Could it be that everything was not lost after all? But why was the Earl of Warwick helping him? Warwick had a genuine claim to the throne, whereas he, Perkin, had publicly confessed to being an impostor! Could it be a trick of some sort? If so, what could they hope to gain by it? Warwick, too, would be in serious trouble if they were caught. None of it really made sense. But he had to seize this last throw of the dice that fate had given him – his last chance for freedom.

The voice came again – more insistent than before. 'Perkin. *Do you agree to it?*'

'Yes,' he shouted. 'Yes!'

Suddenly, there was a terrific crash, then a lot of shouting. It came from upstairs, from the Earl of Warwick's cell.

A few heartbeats later Perkin's own cell door was flung open.

He looked up to see four armed guards standing in the doorway. As one of them stepped forward, Perkin felt his knees go weak, as though they were going to give way.

'Perkin Warbeck. I arrest you on a charge of high treason!'

CHAPTER 10

Two days later, Perkin faced trial at Westminster Hall. Outside, the crowds were yelling and shaking their fists.

'Go to hell!' the guards shouted as they threw Perkin into a cell below the hall.

The noise in the hall above began to increase: the galleries were filling up. Suddenly, there was silence. Perkin was led upstairs. Doing his best to adjust his eyes to the light, he saw a procession of clerks, lawyers and judges file into the hall.

The crier called out, 'Pray silence for His Majesty's Justices!'

There was silence for a moment or two, but then people started talking again. 'Silence in court on pain of imprisonment!'

'Bring forth the prisoner, Perkin Warbeck!'

The usher led Perkin into the hall where he made a bow. When he raised his head the first thing he noticed were carvings of guardian angels looking down at him from the beams. Would they protect him now?

One of the judges leant forward and spoke to the crier. 'Have you the charge?'

'It is here, my lord.'

'Then please read it.'

'Perkin Warbeck. You are on trial for high treason… I charge you, Perkin Warbeck of Tournai, an enemy of the King, that you falsely claimed to be Richard, the second son of the late King Edward IV, and tried to bring about the death of King Henry.'

'That's not true!' Perkin shouted. 'It was a trap!'

'Silence!' roared the judge. He turned to the lawyer. 'Go on!'

'At Deal, in Kent, you landed forces to invade England. At Penzance in Cornwall you recruited an army

82

against the King. While you were a prisoner in the Tower of London you conspired to kill the King. How do you answer these charges?'

'Not guilty, your honour. I was not acting of my own free will. Therefore I cannot be held responsible for my actions.'

'Not responsible for your deeds, eh? You mean you're a madman?'

Muffled laughter was heard from the ladies and gentlemen. The judge looked across at Perkin. His expression was grave. 'Perkin Warbeck. Do you have anything to add to your testimony? Do you wish to alter it in any way?'

But Perkin was given no time to answer. The court did not seem interested in anything he had to say in his defence.

'Call forth the witnesses!' shouted the lawyer.

The figure of a man arose from somewhere at the back. 'Robert Cleymond,' the lawyer continued. 'Come into court!'

Cleymond, a skinny, nervous-looking man with a long face, came forward and bowed awkwardly before the court. It was the first time Perkin had ever seen him. Cleymond had really been working for the King: that much was now horribly clear.

'Robert Cleymond. You were kept captive in the same tower as the prisoner. Is that correct?'

'Yes, your honour.'

'Did you witness the prisoner plotting?'

'Indeed yes. The prisoner did frequently communicate with the Earl of Warwick who shared my cell.'

'Communicate? What was the nature of these... er' – he cleared his throat – 'communications?'

'The pair of them were plotting to free the prisoners, set fire to the gunpowder and kill the Constable.'

A gasp went up from the crowd. Perkin jumped to his feet.

'You lie! It was your idea. It was your suggestion.'

'Hold your tongue!' roared the judge. 'How dare you! If we have any further outbursts from you, Warbeck, you will be put in chains!'

The lawyer asked Cleymond to continue.

'They spoke to one another through a hole in the floor of our cell.' He looked Perkin directly in the face. 'They were plotting treason against the King.'

The lawyer turned to the judges and abruptly declared: 'My lords, I have done! It is only too clear that the accused is guilty of treason.'

The judge addressed his colleagues: 'You have now heard evidence of the treachery of this man from the lips of an eyewitness. My lords, please retire to consider your verdict.'

The judges filed out of the room. They were gone for less than an hour. But for Perkin, the wait seemed like an eternity. Eventually they returned and he was called forward.

'Is the prisoner, Perkin Warbeck, guilty or not guilty of the charges laid against him?'

The judge looked across at his colleagues. 'Guilty, my lord!'

'The prisoner has been found guilty of high treason. Before I pass sentence, do you, Perkin Warbeck, have anything to say?'

This time Perkin was determined to be heard. He took a step nearer to the judges, then threw back his head. 'Yes, my lord, I do. I am an innocent man who was led astray by Englishmen – subjects of King Henry. And I ask you: why are they not in court today? Besides which, as a foreigner, I claim immunity from this court. The courts of England cannot try a foreign subject!'

The judge stood, his face red and furious. 'We are astonished that you dare to excuse your conduct in this way. You have conspired against King Henry like a common spy. You are subject to the jurisdiction of this court. You have been found guilty of HIGH TREASON.

The sentence of this court is that you shall be taken from here to the Tower of London and be kept there until a time and a place be appointed for your execution. You will then be taken through the streets of London to Tyburn where you will be hanged and cut down alive. Your bowels will be taken out and burned, your head cut off. Your body will be quartered, and your head and quarters disposed of as the King thinks fit.'

As he left the hall, Perkin wrapped his cloak around him more tightly, the better to hide his trembling limbs. Outside, a crowd jeered and shouted 'Long live King Henry!' A youth spat at him, and the saliva trickled down Perkin's face as he was taken back to his cell in the Tower and put in chains.

* * *

It was the day before Perkin's execution. The stench of sodden rushes covering the floor of his cell made him feel ill. He felt very, very cold and afraid. He prayed for rescue.

All of a sudden he heard hushed voices, then footsteps on the staircase, in the passageway. A key was turned in the lock and his cell door swung open.

'Your wife's come to see yerr!' said the gaoler.

The gaoler stepped aside to reveal Kate. Her complexion was sickly pale. She came towards him and, with a sense of desperate sadness, Perkin took her in his arms and held her close. He could feel her tears against his face. They stood there in each other's arms, in silence. What was there to say?

At last Perkin broke the silence. 'Forgive me. Try to remember the happy times.'

'Forgive me for what I said to you when we last met,' she cried.

'Be brave, my love,' said Perkin. 'My life will soon be at an end but you must go on. You are a young woman, you have many years ahead of you. You will love again. You will marry and have children. Try to forget me.'

'No!' she cried. 'How can I?'

'You will find happiness again, I'm sure of it. I pray that you do.'

Kate raised her head and gazed at Perkin. Her eyes were red from weeping. Into his palm she pressed a gold chain with a crucifix. 'Take this, my dearest, and carry it with you tomorrow.'

It was the chain that she always wore around her neck. Perkin lifted it to his lips and kissed it. What could he give her in return? He had only one thing of value left – his wedding ring. He removed it from his finger and pressed it into her hands.

'Take this, my love, and farewell.'

Suddenly there was the sound of footsteps outside. The gaoler had returned.

'Come on, now. Enough!' he growled.

For a brief moment Kate held Perkin's hand in hers. Then she bent her head and raised his hand to her lips and kissed it.

'Goodbye my love.'

She disappeared from view. The door clanged shut. Perkin was alone.

CHAPTER 11

Shortly before midday, on 23rd November 1499, Perkin Warbeck was taken from the Tower to Tyburn. His head was bowed. But even now he was not without hope. He asked his guards if it was true that some men had been spared at the last minute. Perhaps the King might show mercy. The guards sniggered in reply.

As they approached Tyburn the noise was deafening. Londoners were used to seeing thieves hanged. They were also used to seeing traitors hanged, drawn and quartered. But they showed a special interest in Perkin. They had heard about his bizarre adventures, and there was something that fascinated them about his daring imposture. How could a boatman's son from Tournai end up marrying the King of Scotland's cousin?

Perkin confessed one final time that he was not Richard, Duke of York, that he had no royal blood in him whatsoever, that in reality he was a stranger from overseas. Even at this late hour he believed he might be granted a pardon. At the foot of the gallows he was still hopeful that an order would arrive from the King, and offer him a reprieve – as a man, foreign-born, who had no right to be tried in this country, and who in any case had been led astray by the King's own wayward subjects.

Would the clergymen and friars who stood in front of him plead for him? And what about the crowd itself? Did he have no supporters there?

He looked up. A beam had been placed across the branches of two trees to make a small scaffold. Against the beam was set a ladder, draped with a black cloth. The executioner stood ready. A black mask covered his face.

For much of his life Perkin had been treated as a prince; he was now to suffer the death penalty of a mere commoner. The crowd cheered as a halter was tied around his neck and they went wild when, with a violent spasm, he was raised to hang on the beam above.

The court's instructions were crystal clear: Perkin

would be cut down while still alive, his bowels removed and burned. After that his body would doubtless be buried in an unmarked grave and his head taken in a basket to London Bridge to be put on a long spike as a warning to other traitors.

Suddenly, Perkin's body dropped like a stone, and was left swinging in the cold winter air. The Boy who would be King ended his life in the same way as his adventures had begun, so many years before — as a puppet at the mercy of others.

Quiz

After you've finished the book, test yourself and see how well you remember what you've read.

1. Perkin's mother wanted him to become:
   An explorer who would travel the world
   A banker who would become rich and famous
   A cloth merchant who would settle down and raise a family

2. At the age of 14, Perkin spent his days:
   Working in a market selling fabrics
   Helping in his father's carpet factory
   Bunking off school to play football

3. The Duchess of Burgundy thought that Perkin looked like:
   Her nephew Prince Richard
   The singer Little Richard
   King Richard the Lionheart

4. Charles, King of France made a big impression on Perkin because:
   He was so fat he could hardly move
   He had the muscular frame of a body-builder
   He had a tiny body and a large head

5. In July 1495, Perkin Warbeck decided to invade England by:
   Putting his troops on the Eurostar
   Sailing his ships to Kent in broad daylight
   Swimming across the Channel under cover of darkness

6. When Perkin arrived in Kent, his soldiers were easily defeated because:
   They were feeling seasick

They got drunk on English ale
They had forgotten their weapons

7. King James IV of Scotland was delighted that Perkin showed an interest in:
    His favourite sport of lawn tennis
    The ancient art of haggis-making
    His pretty cousin Katherine Gordon

8. While banquets were taking place, King James's dogs:
    Were chained up outside the Great Hall to keep watch
    Roamed around under the tables looking for scraps
    Performed displays of highland dancing

9. Perkin's second attempt to invade England in 1496 failed because:
    The northern nobles stayed loyal to Henry
    His men all fell ill with food poisoning
    He took the wrong turning and got lost

10. Off the coast of Ireland, Perkin's ships were:
    Boarded by Spanish pirates
    Shipwrecked on the rocks
    Attacked by the kraken

11. When Henry VII's men came aboard the ship, Perkin:
    Jumped overboard and tried to swim to land
    Pretended he was a Spanish merchant
    Hid himself and his wife in wine barrels

12. When Perkin arrived at the fish market in Penzance he:
    Saw there was a good opportunity to sell high-quality Belgian chips
    Proclaimed himself King Richard IV of England
    Bought fresh mackerel for his army's supper

13. The men of Cornwall wanted to fight against the king
because:
    King Henry had voted Miss Cornwall off the Beautiful
    Maids of Britain competition
    They objected to paying taxes that supported Henry's army
    A royal decree banned the sale of Cornish fudge in London

14. When their siege of Exeter was going badly, one of Perkin's
followers suggested:
    Reducing the enemy to helpless laughter by telling jokes
    Constructing a machine to batter down the gates
    Urinating on the enemy's gunpowder

15. Abbot Humphrey of Beaulieu Abbey helped Perkin by pro-
viding him with:
    A month's sanctuary
    A ticket to France
    A monk's habit that he could wear as a disguise

16. When Perkin finally came face to face with Henry VII in
Taunton, he:
    Ran away
    Confessed to plotting against the throne
    Challenged the king to a duel

17. On hearing that he was not really the rightful heir to the
throne of England, Kate's reaction was:
    'You'll always be my prince, my darling.'
    'Get out of my sight. I don't want to see you ever again!'
    'I always thought there was something funny about your
    accent.'

18. During the 15th century, the River Thames was:

A source of clean, fresh water for the people of London
A much-loved leisure resource for weekend boating activities
A smelly public sewer

19. While he was imprisoned in the Tower of London, Perkin was tricked into:
    A round-the-world cruise scam
    Yet another plot against the crown
    Buying a new life insurance policy

20. The usual penalty for traitors such as Perkin was death by:
    Being hanged, drawn and quartered
    Being buried alive
    Being burned at the stake

Acknowledgements

Lots of people helped with this book and I should like to thank them all – first and foremost Diana Williams for her advice and infinite patience in reading all the drafts; also the children who read the book and made many useful comments – Josh Costello, Lauren Mallett, Sophie Pout, Michael Turrell and Charles Willett.

Key dates

1474 – Perkin Warbeck is born in Tournai, Flanders

1485 – Henry VII is crowned King of England. Prince Edward
and Prince Richard disappear

1491 – Duchess Margaret of Burgundy trains Perkin to pose as
the lost prince

1492 – Perkin is sent to Cork

1493 – King Charles VIII of France summons Perkin to Paris

1495, July – Perkin attempts an invasion at Deal, Kent; Nov –
Perkin is welcomed by King James IV in Scotland

1496, January – Perkin marries Catherine Gordon; Sept – he
makes his second attempt to invade England

1497, Sept – Perkin lands in Cornwall disguised as Richard,
the Duke of York; Oct – he is forced to surrender to
King Henry VII at Taunton

1498 – Plot to blow up Tower of London

1499 – Perkin is found guilty of high treason; he is later
hanged at Tyburn